KALMUS STUDY SCORES

No. 803

WOLFGANG AMADEUS
MOZART

THE PIANO SONATAS AND FANTASIES

IN TWO VOLUMES

VOLUME I

K 279 - K 284, K309 - K 311, K 330, K 547a

WOLFGANG AMADEUS MOZART
(1756-1791)

THE PIANO SONATAS and FANTASIES

The first 6 of MOZART'S 18 Piano Sonatas were all written in 1774 in Salzburg (K 279-284.)They are relatively unimportant, but are written in the elegant, somewhat superficial style of the period.

Sonata K 310 written in 1778 is the only one until K 457 which is written in minor key. It shows already in the few years of interval the great advance in style and maturity of the composer.

Two sonatas were written in 1777 the D major K 311 and the F major K 332. Following this comes one of the most played and popular sonatas, the A major sonata K 331. It is remarkable in its form. Instead of a regular first movement it contains a theme followed by variations. It was written in 1778.

Chronologically the Fantasies K 394, 397, 496 follow the K 331 sonata. They were written in Vienna around 1780. The Sonata K 457 and Fantasy K 475 were also composed in Vienna 1784 to 1785 respectively and are followed by Sonatas K 545 (facile) 1788, and K 570 and 576 in 1789. These two are Mozart's last piano sonatas.

The K numbers mean the numbers in the list of MOZART'S works made by Ludwig, Ritter von Koechel, an Austrian musician in 1862.

TABLE OF CONTENTS

VOLUME I

(Kalmus No. 803)

VOLUME II

(Kalmus No. 804)

Sonate

W. A. Mozart, K.V. 279

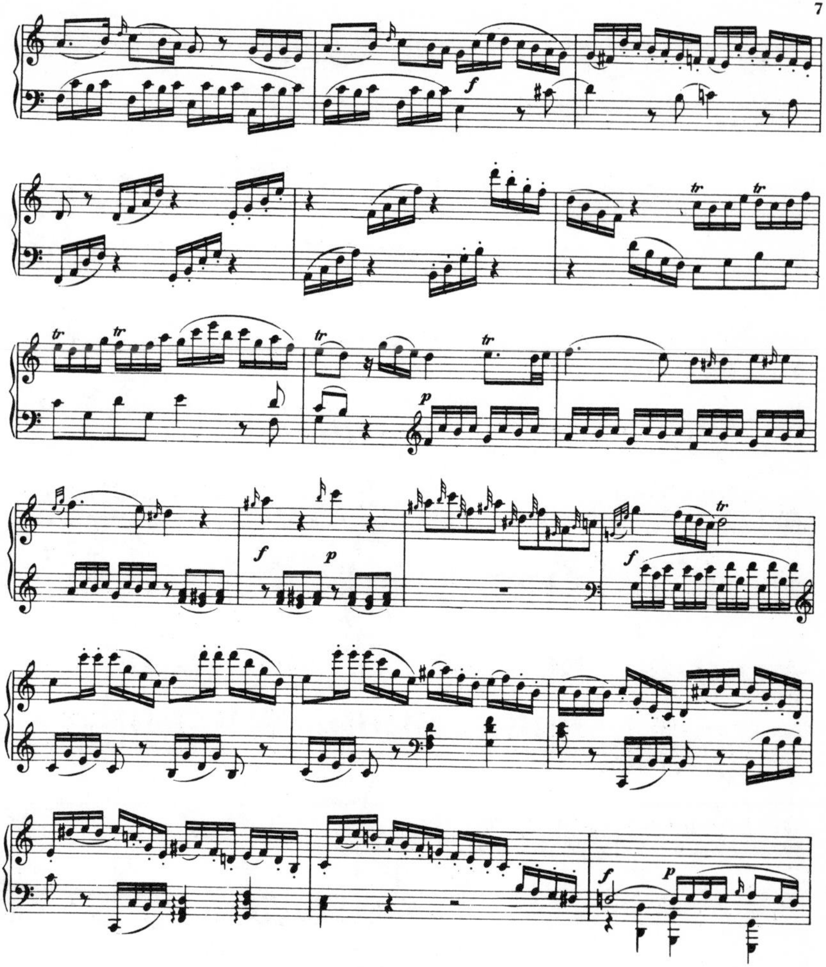

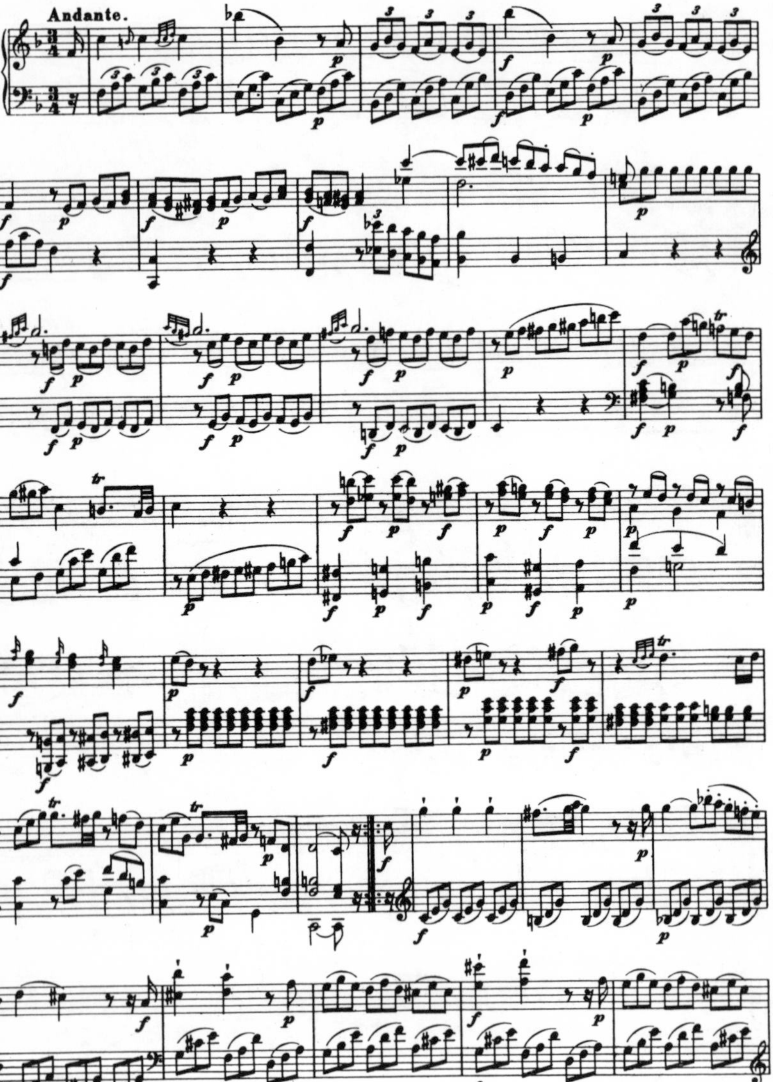
Andante.

Allegro.

12

Sonate

W. A. Mozart, K. V. 280

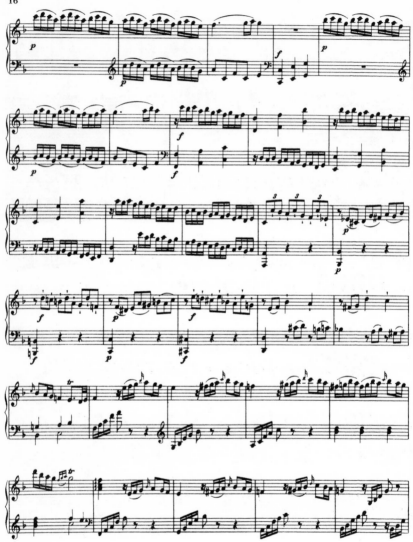

18

Presto.

Sonate

W. A. Mozart, K.V. 281

3.

Andante amoroso.

Rondo.
Allegro.

Sonate

W. A. Mozart, K.V. 282

4.

Menuetto I.

Menuetto II.

Men. I. da Capo.

Sonate

W. A. Mozart, K.V. 283

40

46

Sonate

W. A. Mozart, K.V. 284

49

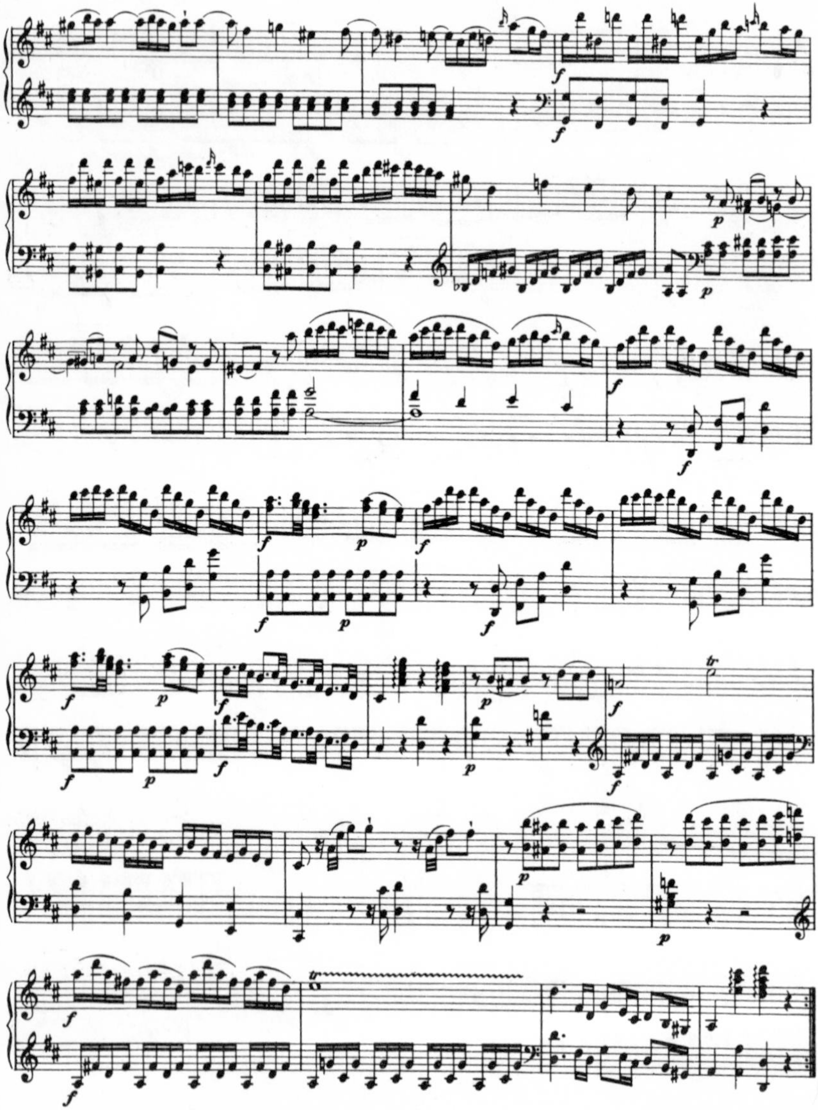

Rondeau en Polonaise.

Andante.

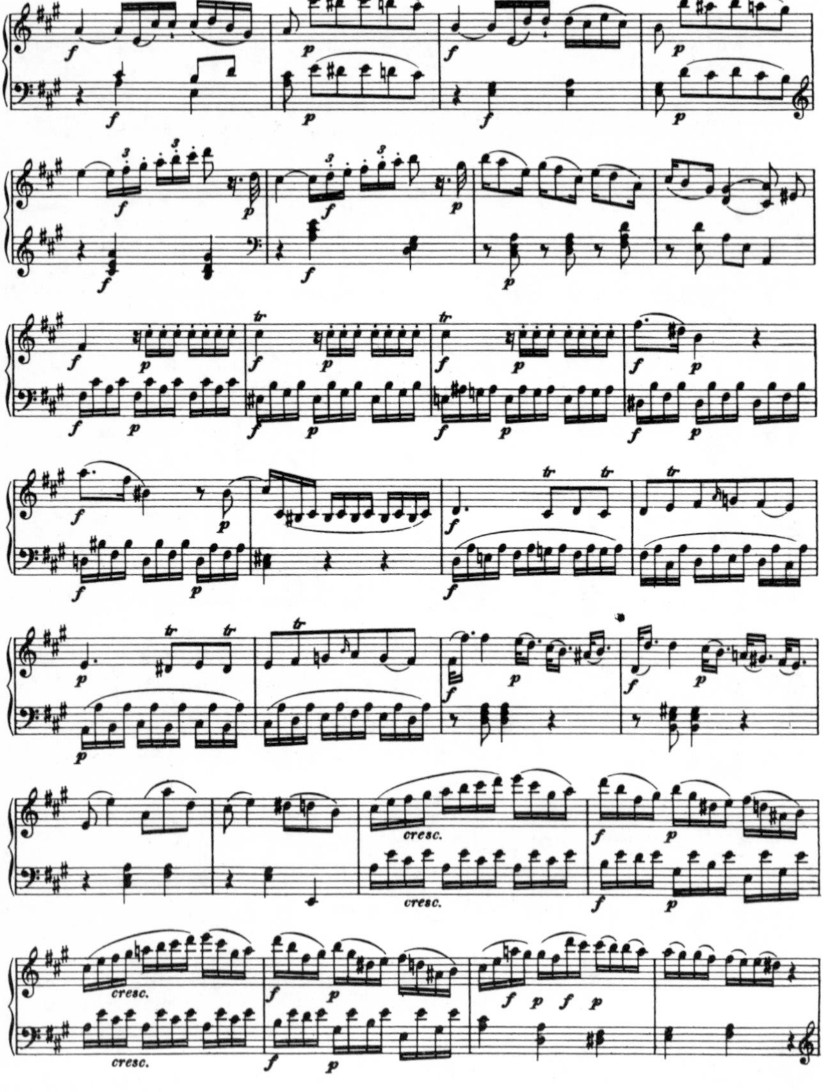
cresc.
cresc.
cresc.
cresc.

Var. VII.
Minore.

Var. VIII.
Maggiore.

64

*) Die eingeklammerten Vortragsbezeichnungen nach der Torricella'schen Ausgabe.

Var. XII.
(Allegro.)

Sonate

W. A. Mozart, K. V. 309

7. Allegro con spirito.

Same as b1-8

Andante un poco adagio.

Rondo.
Allegretto grazioso.

Sonate

W. A. Mozart, K. V. 310
Komponiert 1778 in Paris

Allegro maestoso.

8.

*) Im Autograph sind die nächsten 8 Takte nicht ausgeschrieben, sondern nur durch „*Da Capo 8 mesures*" angedeutet; möglich, dass die Vorschlagsnote *Dis* hier fortfallen sollte.

Andante cantabile con espressione.

90

Sonate

W. A. Mozart, K.V. 311

Allegro con spirito.

9.

Andante con espressione.

Rondo.
Allegro.

Sonate

W. A. Mozart, K.V. 330

10.

Vorlagen: Autograph und die älteste von Mozart selbst bei Artaria in Wien veranlasste Ausgabe; ausserdem die alte Ausgabe von Breitkopf & Härtel. Die eingeklammerten Vortragszeichen finden sich erst bei Artaria.

118

SONATE

TEMA.
Allegretto.

VAR.I.

VAR. II.

VAR. III.

VAR. VI.
Maggiore.